Chairman, Friends of Finchley Memorial Hospital

The Friends of Finchley Memorial Hospital are de
of this history of the hospital to mark its first hundrec

We are very grateful to Friern Barnet & District Local History Society for initiating the project and to their member, Dorrell Dressekie, for undertaking the daunting task of researching and writing up a very comprehensive and readable account of the hospital. It is a worthy memento to our unique hospital.

We cannot say what the future holds. But we are very optimistic about Barnet Primary Care Trust's plans to develop the hospital as a modern healthcare facility fit for purpose and meeting the changing healthcare needs of the local population. We will spare no effort in our voluntary capacity to work with the Trust towards that goal.

Peter Packer
Chairman
Friends of Finchley Memorial Hospital

Chairman Friern Barnet & District Local History Society

One of the fascinating things about the study of local history is that it enables us to learn not only the bare facts, but also the picture of the way that people lived and worked and what shaped their everyday lives.

From the early days of Finchley Memorial, when it was founded by local people and subsequently supported by their financial contributions, to the present day reminiscences of its users, there runs a golden thread which shows that it is, above all, an institution that has been much loved by the community it serves.

It is fascinating to look back on those early days when the residents of Finchley and the surrounding area fought long and hard for something that meant so much to them and it is heartening that in the modern era the work of the hospital has been praised by the upper echelons of the National Health Service. The first hundred years has been a triumph; let us hope that history will record that the second hundred was even better.

David Berguer
Chairman
Friern Barnet & District Local History Society

Chair of Barnet Primary Care Trust

I am delighted to welcome this book, which tells the impressive story of
Finchley Memorial Hospital.

It is a story of many chapters but with a common theme: the commitment of local
people to a local hospital. From the early days of planning, through two World Wars
and into the era of the NHS, this book tells the tale of dedicated individuals and
groups from the local community such as the Friends of Finchley Memorial
Hospital and from the health professions coming together to meet the changing
healthcare needs of the local population. The partnership of local people and
health professionals has served Finchley Memorial Hospital well over the last
hundred years, and will, I believe, continue to play a crucial role in its future.

May I also extend a personal thank you both to Dorrell Dressekie for compiling this
history, and to all the people of Finchley who have worked and continue to work so
hard for Finchley Memorial Hospital.

Sally Malin
Chair
Barnet Primary Care Trust

Finchley Memorial Hospital 1908 to 2008

Introduction

Acknowledgements

Sources of Research

Introduction

In 1908 Finchley Cottage Hospital opened in Finchley to provide healthcare for the residents of Finchley and the surrounding neighbourhood.

This brief history, researched by a member of Friern Barnet and District Local History Society, chronicles the development of the hospital from those early years to the present as it completes one hundred years in meeting health needs of the local community.

The story is recounted as far as possible, within the historical context of each era, noting the impact on the hospital of some government changes in the structure and management of healthcare and some economic and technical changes that determine the provision of healthcare to the local community. Population changes, consequences of two world wars, the coming of a national health service and changing views on provision of healthcare generally, are all included.

In researching the history it became evident quite early on that, while it was a story about a hospital, it was also that of a community working together in response to a need they identified. There was no hospital in the vicinity and the decision that one should be provided led initially to a group of public spirited residents of Finchley and surrounding districts to commence discussion on such a project. The efforts and contributions of those public spirited residents were found to be well documented. Yet a whole community had united, pooled their efforts and contributed according to their means so a hospital could be built.

The Friends of Finchley Memorial Hospital uphold that community involvement. By voluntary efforts and fundraising they help with the purchase of equipment, meet costs of some new buildings and refurbishment of others, all to ensure patients have the benefits of extra comfort and are cared for in a pleasant environment. The Friends have existed for fifty years and it can be said that their involvement and commitment have contributed overwhelmingly to how the hospital is viewed today: a unique, much loved and valued community facility.

Acknowledgements

I offer thanks to everyone who helped me to produce this short history of Finchley Memorial Hospital.

It would not have been possible without the encouragement of the Committee of the Friern Barnet & District Local History Society all of whom were very supportive and helped throughout with advice, with publicity and for sharing their knowledge of the hospital. Special thanks to John Holtham, committee member, for photographic and scanning work, to David Berguer and Peter Packer for proof reading and to Michael Nash for general assistance in preparation of text.

The Friends of Finchley Memorial Hospital have given their assistance without reserve. Their knowledge of the whole hospital environment and of the changes over time has helped significantly as have their loan of books, pamphlets and newsletters.

Barnet Archives has proved a most valuable resource, and the timely help of the Archivist, Yasmine Webb, cannot be overstated.

Thanks to members of staff at the hospital and members of the Friends who have loaned photographs from their personal collection.

Thanks to the hospital management for allowing me access to information, for the helpful contribution from the hospital administrator Linda Stevens, and to the staff in general for a friendly welcome to the hospital.

The anecdotal comments and reminiscences from local residents, from patients and their relatives and carers and from employees, present and former, have added the very significant human dimension to this story. Thanks to all.

Dorrell Dressekie
May 2008

Sources of Research

1. Hospital Records and Health Authority records, made openly available to me
2. Minutes of meetings of hospital's Committee of Management (Hand written records)
3. Minutes of Friern Barnet Urban District Council (London Borough of Barnet Archives Resource)
4. Minutes and Annual Reports of Barnet Community Health Council (London Borough of Barnet Archives Resource)
5. Minutes of Meetings of Friends of Finchley Memorial Hospital
6. Newsletters of Friends of Finchley Memorial Hospital
7. Numerous other Resources of London Borough of Barnet Archives
8. Press Reports from Colindale News Paper Library, Branch of British Library
9. King's Fund Reference Library: Historical records of Hospital Development and of Voluntary Hospitals in particular
10. London Metropolitan Archives: Hospital records
11. Memories: Photographic Reproduction and Local History Specialist

Oral and anecdotal comments have been obtained from a number of sources. They include comments and reminiscences from Members of the Friern Barnet & District Local History Society, Members of the Friends of Finchley Memorial Hospital and some present and former employees of the hospital. Also helpful have been the comments from local residents, some of them former patients and many of whom have been familiar with the hospital over several years, and others who now use the facilities and are benefiting from the services it provides.

ERAS: Pre War

1904 to 1908

Opening of Cottage Hospital 1908
Planning Stage 1904 to Opening in 1908

Financial Support and Ongoing Maintenance
Internal Working of Hospital
A Complaint

1909 to 1918

Fundraising and Challenges of War

Death of a President
Discussion of Hospital Extensions and First World War

1919 to 1922

War Memorial Extension

1923 to 1933

Era of Growth and Challenges

Financing Proposed Extension

1934 to 1938

Some Trying Times and Financial Hardship

1939 to 1945

Second World War

Opening of Cottage Hospital 1908

In 1908 a hospital with 20 beds, named then Finchley Cottage Hospital, opened for the reception and treatment of patients residing in the district of Finchley and surrounding neighbourhood. The need for a hospital was identified in 1897. In the book titled, *Barnet Voices 1999 Recollections of Local People*, [1] compiled by historian Percy Reboul, it is stated, 'the idea for a local hospital to serve the people of Finchley and surrounding neighbourhood was first conceived during the celebrations of Queen Victoria Jubilee 1897'.

The population, legislated for by the Urban District of Finchley, was estimated then as 33,000 and there was no hospital in their immediate neighbourhood to serve their need. That need inspired a group of residents to take the initiative to begin discussing the idea of building a hospital in their midst.

Planning Stage:
1904 to its opening in 1908

Planning Stage 1904

Discussions began in a humble way, their first meeting, attended by eight people, taking place in a room over the shop of one Mr Danby, a saddler, at 59 High Road, North Finchley and who was a member of the local Tradesmen Association.

A public meeting held by the group of residents on Tuesday June 14, 1904, gave a major leap to the initial discussions with the unanimous agreement 'that a Cottage Hospital was urgently needed and that the time had arrived to provide such an institution'.

A general committee and various sub-committees were then set up to plan and take forward the next stage. The committees consisted of local residents who were interested in the project, owners of some local businesses, members of the Rate Payers Association and medical practitioners residing or practicing in the district.

[1] Barnet Voices, 1999, Recollections of Local People. Historian: Percy Reboul

They held several meetings over the period of a year, discussing aspects such as size of the hospital, the cost, how the necessary funds could be raised and how to encourage public support. Full statement of their deliberation was presented at a further public meeting held on Thursday June 29 1905 in the Council Offices based at Church End, Finchley. [2]

Finchley Cottage Hospital.

A PUBLIC MEETING

Will be held at the District Council Offices, Church End,

On THURSDAY, 29th JUNE, 1905, at 8 p.m.

SIR ALFRED DE BOCK PORTER, K.C.B.,

IN THE CHAIR.

The following Statement will be submitted by the Committee:

"Now that a year has elapsed since the project of providing a Cottage Hospital for the district of Finchley was seriously taken in hand, the Committee charged with the business desire to place before the inhabitants of the locality the following statement:—

"It will be remembered that, at a Public Meeting on the 14th June, 1904, it was unanimously resolved 'That a Cottage Hospital is urgently needed, and that the time has arrived to provide such an Institution.'

"For the purpose of giving effect to that Resolution, a General Committee and requisite Sub-Committees were at once formed, and several conferences took place between the principal persons known to be favourable to the project and representatives of the medical men residing or practising in the district, with the result that it was decided to endeavour to provide a Hospital to contain 20 beds, at an estimated cost (exclusive of the site) of about £5,000.

"In coming to that decision the Committee were influenced by what they believed to be the requirements of the district, as well as by the most generous offer of Mr. Ebenezer Homan to provide a site of two acres for the Hospital (at a cost of £1,000), provided adequate funds for the erection of the building were raised within a reasonable period.

"As regards the site, the Ecclesiastical Commissioners have agreed to sell for the purposes of the Hospital, at any time within the next two years, two acres of land on the highest part of their Fallow Corner Estate, a site which the Committee have chosen as being conveniently situated

[2] The Finchley Press, Friern Barnet Press, Muswell Hill Mercury, May 29, 1908

One important aspect agreed at the onset of their discussions was the determination not to begin work on building a hospital until the money required for the purpose was collected. The estimated cost then, exclusive of site, was £5000. One member of the Committee, Mr Ebenezer Homan, made the generous offer to purchase a site on condition that adequate funds for erection of the building could be raised within a reasonable period. He conveyed to the appointed Trustees the sum of £1000, subject to compliance that an adequate sum for erection of the proposed building be raised before 30th June 1907.

The site chosen for the hospital was on land situated at the highest point of the Fallow Farm Estate near the Great North Road as it crossed Finchley. The Committee agreed 'it being conveniently situated almost in the centre of the district and very eligible in all respects'.

The land was owned by the Ecclesiastical Commissioners who agreed the sale of two acres. With purchase of the land secured, the task of raising funds began in earnest. Contact was made with every household through circular letters and personal canvassing house to house. The public response, thought slow at first, gained momentum with fundraising functions and voluntary contributions increasing, as if everyone was desirous of taking part in the project. Mention was made, for example, of subscriptions received from the working men who started making regular payments to the fund by setting up a special Working Men's Cottage Hospital Fund. The amount they added to the fund quite early on was recorded as £169.8s.5d.

The generous public response made it possible within a short space of time for the Committee to appoint architects for the design and drawing up of plans and enter into contract with builders. The architects for the design were Messrs E. I'Anson and partner Mr Hazelhurst, designers of St Bartholomew's Hospital. The builders were Messrs T H and F Higgs.

PROGRAMME.

LIBERTY HALL.

An Original Modern Play in Four Acts,

BY

R. C. CARTON.

- PERFORMANCE -

IN AID OF THE FUND TOWARDS THE ERECTION OF A

FINCHLEY COTTAGE HOSPITAL,

AT THE

Woodside Hall,

NORTH FINCHLEY N.

Friday Evening, December 30th, 1904, at 8.15 p.m.

The building took shape rapidly and Finchley Cottage Hospital was completed and opened to the public on Thursday May 28, 1908. It had 20 beds, 10 for men, 8 for women, 2 isolation beds, and stood in beautiful grounds designed by Finchley Horticultural Society. On May 29, 1908, the Finchley Press, Muswell Hill Mercury and Highgate Post reported 'Amid much éclat, and in the presence of nearly 500 invited guests, Finchley Cottage Hospital, situated in Granville-road and Bow-lane, was yesterday thrown open to public inspection. The guests were accommodated in a large marquee, which resembled rather a large concert hall than a tent, and so well were arrangements made that not the slightest hitch occurred, everything passing off as merrily as the ringing of the marriage bell'. [3]

Mr Ebenezer Homan, who presided over the opening ceremony, was presented with a gold key by the Architects for the special opening of the main door to the hospital. The key can be viewed today in a cabinet located in the main entrance foyer of the hospital.

In his opening address to the gathering Mr Homan made reference to the community spirit that enabled the building of the hospital, of the army of volunteers unselfishly working in the good cause for several years and of everyone in the parish making some contribution to what has been achieved, a splendid building, well furnished, perfectly equipped and starting out clear of debt.

[3] The Glebe Lands (London Borough of Barnet Archives)

Opening Ceremony, Finchley Cottage Hospital, May 28th, 1908

Financial support and ongoing maintenance

Initiatives announced at the opening ceremony were the setting up of an Endowment Fund to secure the future of the hospital and a Samaritan Fund to which contributions were invited. The Hospital Fund, set up during the process of building, was kept open for donations and businesses and individuals invited to sign up as Annual Subscribers.

Internal Working of the Hospital

The Committee of Management, as governing body of the hospital, proceeded with the setting up of a number of sub-committees, each with rules and guidance as to their roles and responsibilities.

One of the first of these was the House Committee. The business of this Committee as stated in the minutes of the Committee of Management, July 1, 1908, was 'for the purpose of regulating and controlling the details of matters relating to the internal administration of the hospital and the conduct of its affairs and business generally'. [4]

Next were Collection Committees. For this, members of the Committee of Management were divided according to the area in which they resided, to take the lead in setting up these committees. The business of Collection Committees was to obtain promises of annual subscriptions and donations from persons in their respective neighbourhood, and to put in place suitable arrangements for collecting funds. The first areas to set up Collection Committees were Oakleigh Park, Whetstone, North Finchley, Church End and East Finchley.

Other Sub-Committees included a Ladies Committee, Ladies Collecting Guild, Trustee for the Samaritan Fund and a rota for Monthly Visitors. The Monthly Visitors, two or three persons at each visit, were given a number of responsibilities. They would meet with the medical staff to discuss and agree admission and discharge of patients, to assess what payment, if any, a patient could pay towards the cost of treatment, the length of stay in hospital and to ensure, that on discharge from hospital, each patient had a place to which to return.

The visitors were not in charge of medical matters. That responsibility rested with the medical staff, some local general practitioners, the Matron and her team of nursing staff. The first Matron of the hospital, Miss Adelaide Clark, came to the post from St Bartholomew's Hospital, London.

[4] Source: Minutes of Committee of Management Meeting, July 1st, 1908

The era ended with the dream of a hospital in Finchley becoming a reality, medical, nursing and domestic staff in post in readiness to receive their first patients. The Finchley Press June 12, 1908, reported that the first operation had taken place and proved highly successful. [5]

A Complaint

A complaint was soon to follow however. It is on record that an inquiry was held at Friern Barnet Urban District Council Offices on November 23, 1908 after the relatives of a patient who died in the hospital expressed their concern that attention given to the patient was not as careful as it should have been. The Coroner's letter to the Committee of Management, following the inquiry, stated that the Jury carefully considered everything that was said and agreed unanimously that every attention had been given by the medical and nursing staff and that the unfavourable comments were unjustifiable. They further gave practical exhibition of their feeling on the matter by requesting the foreman of the Jury to forward their fees for the day to the hospital fund. [6]

1909 to 1918
Fundraising and Challenges of War

As stated, the hospital relied on financial support from residents of the district and surrounding neighbourhood. Minutes of meetings of the Committee of Management and of some of the Sub-Committees, recorded during the early years give insight into the numerous fundraising activities within the community, all in aid of maintenance and upkeep. Annual Subscribers signed up and voluntary donations came from a range of sources. Mention has been made of churches holding special Hospital Sundays when all collection would go to the hospital. Prize winning allotment holders donated their winnings. A school children's Cot Fund was set up and maintained by fundraising activities of children in Elementary Schools in Finchley.

[5] Source: Finchley Press June 12th, 1908
[6] Source: Minutes of Committee of Management Meeting, December 30th, 1908

The Ladies Committee held fundraising events such as 'Egg Appeal and Pound Day' when gifts were brought in and sold, and they supervised a needle work guild that made garments for use by patients.

Two beds were maintained by the annual Hospital Carnival. This carnival, later named Finchley Carnival, continues each year in Finchley. Finance committee records also showed that patients paid towards their stay in hospital, the amount agreed according to their means.

Death of the President

In March 1909 the death of Mr Ebenezer Homan was announced. Mr Homan was a major benefactor and one of the founding members of the hospital. In recognition of his contribution it was agreed at the Annual General Meeting of Subscribers held April 1909, that a suitable tablet in his memory be made and placed in the entrance hall of the hospital. In the minutes of the Annual General Meeting of March 31, 1910, there was mention of the bronze bust being placed in the vestibule of the hospital.

Discussion of Hospital Extension and First World War

The monthly statistics of patients' activity began to show, as early as 1910, that a hospital with 20 beds was too small in comparison to the work it was undertaking. The Annual Report, dated December 31, 1910, stated the hospital as full, of patients frequently waiting for vacant beds and of emergency cases being turned away. [7]

The hospital was maintained by contributions from annual subscribers and voluntary donations. The statements of income and expenditure, presented monthly by the Treasurer, showed that such funds were only just adequate to meet upkeep and maintenance needs. Despite the problem of finance however, the Committee of Management raised the issue in 1912 of enlarging the hospital and began discussions on how the funds could be raised.

[7] Source: Annual Report of Finchley Cottage Hospital, December 31st, 1910

At that time, however, another problem was on the horizon which brought a halt to all discussions. The Government declared war with Germany on Tuesday August 4, 1914. The enormous upheaval this was to have on the whole country is well documented, and the hospital in particular was faced with many challenges.

The immediate impact was evident. Minutes of meetings of the Committee of Management, for example, recorded the depletion in staff numbers, as some resigned from their jobs in order to enter war service.

The hospital was requested by the War Refugee Committee to provide medical care for Belgian refugees who sought refuge in Finchley when Belgium was struck during the war. That extra work had to be undertaken in addition to meeting the continuing needs of the local civilian sick.

Some injured solders were treated at two other local hospitals, King Edward's Hall Auxiliary Military Hospital in Church End Finchley, and Summerlee Auxiliary Hospital in East Finchley, while all dependents of serving soldiers were treated free of cost at the Cottage Hospital. But the work that could be undertaken was hampered by lack of equipment such as X-ray apparatus. However, in response to public appeal, sufficient funds were raised and by 1916 X-ray equipment was installed.

In that same year, 1916, the Gardener's Guild was formed, and with assistance of boys from local schools, began cultivating spare land surrounding the hospital and vegetables were grown for the patients.

The Armistice, signed in November 1918, ended the era and the proposals to enlarge the hospital resumed.

1919 to 1922:
War Memorial Extension

With the Great War ended, the Committee of Management resumed the discussion on raising funds to enlarge the hospital, but it was now classified as The War Memorial Fund. This was in line with the thinking that the Cottage Hospital should be a memorial to the men of Finchley who had died in the war.

The Committee of Management also decided to request the cooperation of Friern Barnet Urban District Council and Finchley Urban District Council to make the scheme for the extension a joint effort. This took into account the proximity of Friern Barnet, part of which was already in the area served by the hospital and also the approaching fusion of the two Districts, Finchley and Friern Barnet, as the Parliamentary Constituency of Finchley.

Response to the request was positive and a group consisting of members of the two Urban District Councils, members of the Hospital Committee, Honorary Medical staff and prominent citizens from outside organisations, came together to collaborate on the proposal for the extension.

An early action agreed by this joint group was to propose to the residents of Finchley and Friern Barnet that the extension of the hospital be classified as the War Memorial Extension. The building fund was re-opened and on February 5, 1919 a public meeting was held to consider what form the Finchley War Memorial should take.

The interest generated at that meeting from some prominent residents, and from the community generally, was such that the following motions were put forward and agreed 'That the Town's meeting approves of the extension of the Cottage Hospital becoming Finchley War Memorial'.

'That a joint committee consisting of six members appointed by the Urban District Councils and six appointed by the Hospital Committee of Management be formed to collect on behalf of the Trustees of the Hospital the necessary funds by voluntary contributions for the purpose, towards which the hospital Committee had already acquired or been promised amount to the total of £1,500'. [8]

---

[8] Source: Minutes of Committee of Management Meetings, 1918 to 1922 (Handwritten)

Initial estimates indicated that £10,000 would be needed for building, furnishing and essential endowment of the building. But as discussions progressed and the plans were considered in more detail, that amount was found to be substantially below requirement. The war had resulted in considerable hardship for everyone. The Committee of Management had to grapple with the problem of rising costs of material, of rising salaries and wages and ensuring expenditures were kept as low as was conducive to the wellbeing of patients in their care. But encouraged by popular support, plans were put in motion to raise funds for enlargement of the hospital. The scheme was now classified as the War Memorial Extension and this fundraising campaign was rigorous. The Local Press carried advertisements, Annual Subscribers were sent circulars, collection boxes were placed in trade premises, fundraising functions were arranged by several community groups and general appeal went out to everyone to contribute. The Finance Committee kept meticulous accounts, reporting on regular basis to the Committee of Management as to the state of the funds.

Around this time the hospital received a welcome boost to its finances. The Summerlee Auxiliary Hospital in East Finchley closed and its Committee and Subscribers donated the contents of a twenty bed unit and some operating theatre equipment to the Cottage Hospital, and the sum of £1,000 to the War Memorial Extension Fund. The King Edward's Hospital Fund for London, the organisation with responsibility for procedures and standards relating to Voluntary Hospitals and allocation of financial grants, distributed £250,000 to all such hospitals. Finchley Cottage Hospital received £1,750 from that source.

By 1921 building contracts were agreed and work began on the extension. Progress was rapid and within a short space of time the new building was ready for occupation. The extended hospital contained in total 47 beds a male ward with 10 beds, a female ward with 16 beds, children's ward with 12 beds and a private ward of 9 beds.

The wards were named in recognition of persons whose involvement helped to make the hospital a reality, Homan Ward after the benefactor Mr Ebenezer Homan and Woodrow Ward after the first chairman of the Committee of Management, Mr E A E Woodrow. The children's ward, Summerlee, was perhaps so named in recognition of the 20 bed unit donated to the hospital on the closure of the Summerlee Auxiliary Hospital.

The annual report of that year made proud mention of the fact that all work involved in construction of the extension was undertaken by local firms. The architects, contractors, builders and labourers were all from Finchley and surrounding districts.

The following news item appeared in the Times on November 22, 1922, 'Finchley Cottage Hospital Extension was dedicated on Saturday by the Bishop of Willesden in memory of the men of Finchley and Whetstone who fell in the war, and a memorial tablet was unveiled by Sir Ian Hamilton'. [9]

[9] Source: The Times, November 22, 1922

1923 to 1933:
Era of Growth and Challenges

With changing local conditions such as projections of population growth, there was increasing awareness that future extension of the hospital was inevitable. The Committee of Management, in anticipation of that, had already decided to purchase a further two acres of land. The owners, Ecclesiastical Commissioners were, at that time, selling land for building development on both sides of the hospital. So decision to acquire the extra land was perhaps a precautionary measure to protect the hospital site. But the additional land also provided more garden and open air recreational space for patients. The purchase price was £2000, towards which the King Edward's Hospital Fund for London made a grant of £800.

A Sub-Committee, titled Extension Sub-Committee, was set up to identify future building requirements, prepare reports for the Committee of Management and liaise with architects and builders. The hospital medical staffs were represented on this new Sub-Committee.

One proposal put forward quite early by the extension sub-committee was for the building and staffing of a casualty block. The need for such a facility was quite evident, given the location of the hospital near the Great North Road and at the junction of two main roads, an area prone to accidents. Victims of road accidents were brought in on a regular basis but the hospital lacked adequate space to accommodate them, or staff in sufficient numbers to administer the care they needed.

The Committee of Management agreed, after some discussion, to proceed with such a building. The necessary funds were raised and by 1926 a casualty block and two wards, Mary Curtis and Walter Cope wards, and a casualty operating theatre were built and additional X-ray equipment in place. The main driveway was extended and a separate entrance to the casualty wards provided access for ambulances thus enabling prompt attention to victims of accidents and emergencies, with little or no disturbance to other patients.

Public opening of the casualty block took place on Thursday February 24, 1927 by Lady Barratt, with service of dedication conducted by the Lord Bishop of Willesden. [10]

---

[10] The Glebe Lands (London Borough of Barnet Archives)

The next consideration was the provision of additional accommodation for the nursing staff. In 1922 when the hospital was increased to 47 beds, the staff comprised of a matron, four staff nurses, seven probationers and a small team of domestic staff, a cook, ward maid and a kitchen maid. They were provided with dining and recreational facilities in the re-furbished Summerlee Children's ward, but no additional bedrooms.

Summerlee children's ward was rebuilt around this period. The original had a leaking roof and had to be closed as the medical staff found it unsuitable for treatment of patients, especially children. The original one was then re-furbished and equipped to provide dining and recreational facilities. Sleeping accommodation was made available for some nurses in neighbouring houses but this was found to be not very suitable.

The Committee of Management, after some discussion, agreed at a meeting held May 21, 1928 that active steps be taken for provision of nurses' residence. The Extension Sub-Committee was once again requested to discuss the matter fully, consult architects, have plans prepared and provide estimates of cost.

The plans were much enlarged during the discussion period. In addition to the nurses' home, proposals were included for resident medical officers' accommodation and for a ward of 26 beds for private patients. Plans for a maternity block were also added at the request of medical staff who expressed the view that there was need for such a facility. The new plans were prepared in full consultation with architects, members of the medical team and with the finance committee on July 5, 1928. [11]

Financing the Proposed Extension

For financial help to meet the cost, the plans were submitted to the King Edward's Hospital Fund for London to request a grant. The Distribution Committee of the Fund responded in terms that no objection was raised to the proposals laid out in the plans for nurses' home, beds for private patients and medical officers' accommodation, 'provided that the Committee of Management of the hospital are satisfied as to the prospect of the provision of the necessary funds, both for capital expenditure and future maintenance'. [12]

[11] Minutes of Committee of Management Meeting, July 5th, 1928
[12] King Edward's Hospital Fund for London Distribution Committee, July 22, 1929

The evident conclusion to such response was that there was no prospect of a grant from that source. The plans for the maternity block were sent to Finchley Urban District Council for attention of the Public Health Committee and to the Maternity Department of the Ministry of Health in connection of possible grants.

Neither of these channels however held out much prospect for funds. Reply from the Urban District Council stated that in view of the powers of the County Council under the new Local Government Act, and changes likely to result, the Council was unable to consider any definite steps regarding proposals for a maternity block. [13]

The response from the Maternity Department of the Ministry of Health stated that such grants were not made to Voluntary Hospitals. [14]

Despite these setbacks in obtaining any form of grant, the Committee of Management agreed a start be made on that portion of the building that seemed most urgent. The architects were requested to seek builders' tenders and a start be made on the nurses home, dining room and domestic quarters.

Plans for the maternity block were put on hold on this stage. Members of the medical staff who had put forward the request for a maternity block were asked to reconsider what they felt was necessary in terms of the level of need, the number of maternity beds and special rooms that would be required and the cost effectiveness of the scheme.

The plans for pay beds were accepted, perhaps based on identified needs locally as well as with findings by the King Edward's Hospital Fund for London that showed such beds to be cost effective and very popular elsewhere in the country.

The next avenue in search for funds was to the local inhabitants of Finchley and surrounding districts. Special appeals were circulated with request to contribute as liberally as possible and help to maintain the splendid record of continuing debt free.

[13] Local Government Legislation 1929: The Beginning of Municipal Hospitals
[14] Hospital Committee of Management Meetings, August 1929 to July 1930

Minutes of committee meetings held during the period 1930 to 1932 showed
that quite significant numbers of social activities took place in Finchley and the
surrounding neighbourhood, all in aid of the hospital building fund. Dances,
concerts, garden fetes, billiards, whist drives, bridge and ping pong tournaments,
golf putting competitions and charity performances in local cinemas are among the
many activities on record. A special stone laying ceremony for a new wing of two
wards, Fallowfield and Dickens, was held during the period.

The extension was opened in March 1933 by Lord Horder of Ashford and provided the nursing staff with a dining room, sitting room and increased sleeping accommodation of 14 bedrooms. The new extension also added 26 beds for private patients together with a solarium, but no maternity block.

The hospital had now increased to 72 beds, a Resident Medical Officer was appointed and a number of Honorary Consulting Medical staff availed their services. The population of the district had also grown. The Urban District Council registered a population increase to 62,000.

The need for a hospital mortuary came under discussion around this period. Plans were prepared and following approval by the medical committee, a sterilizing room and mortuary were built.

1934 to 1938: Some Trying Times and Financial Hardship

Criticism and unwelcome publicity nationally was levelled at Finchley Memorial Hospital following an inquest held at Wellhouse Hospital on November 17, 1934 to ascertain the facts regarding the treatment of a patient with burns.

The patient had been taken by ambulance to the hospital. With beds at saturation point, the medical staff examined the patient in the ambulance, and agreed the best course of action was rapid transfer to the Wellhouse where a bed was available. While being attended to in the ambulance the patient requested a drink of water. The doctor attending the patient decided however that, in the best interest of the patient, nothing should be given by mouth. The patient was transferred but did not survive.

The incident was reported in both evening and daily newspapers with sensational headlines of the fatality, using statements such as 'inhumane treatment at Finchley Memorial Hospital' and 'dying girl refused water'. [15]

The Management Committee studied the report of the inquest in detail and penned a letter to the Finchley Press in which the circumstances leading up to such sensational reporting were fully explained. It was the view of the Management Committee, as expressed in the letter, that the medical staff on duty at the time had acted in the best interest of the patient and that their actions were fully justified. Also fully stated in that letter was the commitment on which the hospital prides itself, to be ready and willing at all times to give to casualty cases the prompt care and attention which the nature of their injuries required. [16]

The need for a maternity block was again put forward for discussion by the medical staff. What had emerged by this time, however, was the high probability that Middlesex County Council would build a new general hospital to serve Finchley, Friern Barnet, Hornsey and Wood Green.

[15] The Guardian, November 23, 1934; The Times, November 23, 1934
[16] Letter to Barnet Press from Hospital Committee of Management, November 24th, 1934

The Management Committee, having to consider the effects of such development close to the borders, held lengthy discussions on future policy and the role of Finchley Memorial Hospital on the opening of a new hospital. In the end a hospital was not built and there is no record of any further discussion on a maternity block.

The hospital management faced another critical problem when the Visitors from the King Edward's Hospital Fund for London, in their annual visit report of 1937, commented unfavourably on the accommodation for nurses and maids. The nursing quarters in place in 1933 was already proving too small as numbers of nursing and domestic staff had increased. The Matron had also highlighted the fact that more nurses would be needed as some were working long hours to manage the overcrowding in the wards and to avoid the long wait for patients who needed admission.

A self-contained block of flats adjacent to the hospital was leased and furnished to provide accommodation for the nursing staff but was only short term relief. A more practical arrangement was the decision to purchase a house, 125 Bow Lane in close proximity to the hospital, to provide a more permanent residence. That transaction however, was well on the way to completion when the vendor accepted a higher offer from elsewhere.

The hospital lost one of its major benefactors when the death of Mr E A E Woodward was announced in 1937. He was one of the founding members and first chairman of the hospital's Committee of Management.

Hard times financially were also becoming problematic. Much of the cost for building, maintenance and upkeep during the 1930s was covered by the Annual Subscribers, some generous legacies and from the public in general. But raising adequate funds in this way was becoming increasingly difficult, with a deficit showing in the annual statement of accounts. The shortfall in funds was due to several factors. Upkeep and maintenance costs for the hospital were on the increase. Statements of hospital activity showed rise in the number of patients admitted and more patients treated in casualty as a result of road accidents. Specialisation in types of treatment and at higher cost, and the financial outlay on new technology were all in evidence. The shortage of nursing staff, long working hours for those in post and not so favourable living accommodation for them were all major factors for the management to resolve.

The hospital at this period was, without doubt, in its gravest position financially since its opening in 1908. At the thirtieth Annual General Meeting, April 1938, the president of the hospital, Mr J. F. E. Crowder, commented 'no hospital kept by voluntary contributions nowadays has an easy task to carry on. Finances will always be a difficulty, and just now it is assuming acute form'. [17]

The overwhelming positive aspect for the hospital management, as they grappled through financial hardship and trying times, was probably the continuing involvement of the local community and the help of many volunteers.

Contributions continued from individuals and Annual Subscribers. Funds were raised through activities such as Flag days, Egg Appeal and monthly Pound Days. A Patient's League was formed and some former patients gave funds for much needed ward equipment. Generous donations were made by some local businesses and organisations, for example, the Standard Telephone and Cables Company, the North Middlesex Golf Club and Finchley Rugby Club.

Local cinemas, the Odeon and Coliseum among them, contributed the proceeds of special shows to the hospital and had displays on the screens informing viewers of the hospital fundraising efforts.

Local newspapers, The Hendon Times and Finchley Press, Friern Barnet Press and Muswell Hill Mercury, promoted some of the activities by producing posters and running advertisements of some events.

It was mainly through such support that Finchley Memorial Hospital could pride itself in being independent and able to give the highest quality service to the residents of Finchley and surrounding districts.

However, as the era ended, the continued delivery of such quality service was about to face one of its gravest challenges.

[17] The Finchley Press, Friern Barnet Press, Muswell Hill Mercury, April 22, 1938

GROUND PLAN as at 1938

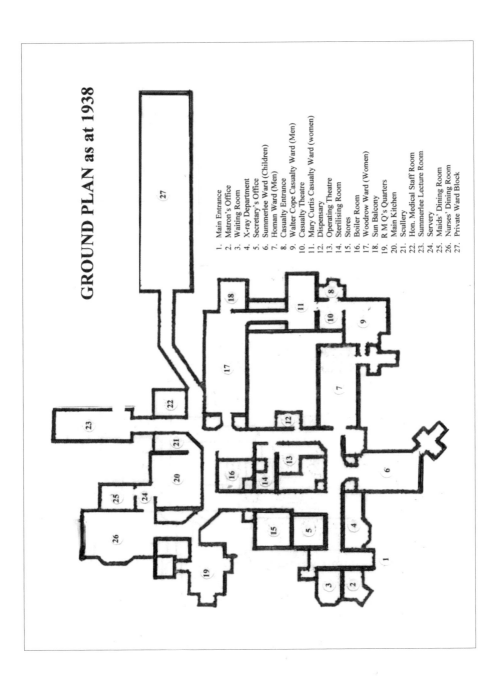

1. Main Entrance
2. Matron's Office
3. Waiting Room
4. X-ray Department
5. Secretary's Office
6. Summerlee Ward (Children)
7. Homan Ward (Men)
8. Casualty Entrance
9. Walter Cope Casualty Ward (Men)
10. Casualty Theatre
11. Mary Curtis Casualty Ward (women)
12. Dispensary
13. Operating Theatre
14. Sterilising Room
15. Stores
16. Boiler Room
17. Woodrow Ward (Women)
18. Sun Balcony
19. R M Q's Quarters
20. Main Kitchen
21. Scullery
22. Hon. Medical Staff Room
23. Summerlee Lecture Room
24. Servery
25. Maids' Dining Room
26. Nurses' Dining Room
27. Private Ward Block

1939 to 1945:
Second World War

For the second time in its history the hospital was put on war time alert when war was declared with Germany in September 1939. Pre-war preparations had began earlier in the year with the Ministry of Health instructions that as many patients as possible should be evacuated so that, in the event of war, beds would be available for air raid victims.

The result of that instruction was that only few civilian patients could be admitted but the full complement of staff had to be maintained.

The Annual Report and Statement of Accounts for year ending December 31, 1939, stated 'No reminder is needed that for the first eight months of the year we were actively engaged in preparing for War, while for the remaining months we were actually at War' and 'These extraordinary circumstances have profoundly affected the statistics of the hospital for the year under review'. [18]

Under the Emergency Hospital Service, a centralised State Agency empowered by the Ministry of Health, Finchley Memorial Hospital was scheduled as a 70 bed Casualty Hospital in Sector 3 of the London area. As such, it was appointed Casualty Receiving Hospital for Finchley and Friern Barnet and assigned a Sector Officer. The Sector Officer was based at the Military Barracks in Mill Hill.

It was a busy and tense period for medical staff as they perfected their plans for war duties and prepared the hospital for reception of casualties. It required a great deal of planning to put in place the various auxiliary services and organize the many volunteers who came individually and from community organizations to offer their services. Minutes of meetings held during the period record the active participation of members of Finchley Rover Scouts, Finchley and Friern Barnet Branch of the British Red Cross, the Gas Officer of Finchley, the Fire Service and in particular many residents who volunteered to be in readiness as blood donors.

---

[18] The Thirty-Second Annual Report of Finchley Memorial Hospital for Year 1939 (London Borough of Barnet Archives)

The stark realisation of the situation at the time can be gleamed from part of the statement in the publication, Finchley Memorial Hospital Your Hospital in War 'On the bright Sunday morning of September 3rd, 1939, we listened [to the radio] in the hospital grounds to the voice of the Prime Minister declaring war upon Germany. Our scouts and helpers paused for a few minutes from the hard work of filling sand-bags and erecting barricades. The tension was emphasised by the memorable alert which followed the broadcast. Within the hospital, the beds in rows stood vacant and ready. All our equipment was distributed and laid out for immediate use. We were ready for action'. [19]

During the early months of the war there were no immediate attacks in the area. As a result staff at the hospital carried on with much of their civilian medical work. But beds were kept vacant as the Ministry of Health instructed, an emergency committee was set up and staff were on the alert at all time to ensure that, should the need arise, they would be ready for action.

Such action began on the night of September 22, 1940 when bombs and incendiaries did reach the hospital borders resulting in injury to several civilians. Some were quite severely wounded, among them children, and all needing immediate attention.

Finchley seldom escaped attacks in the ensuing weeks and admission of casualties became an almost nightly occurrence. The night of November 15, 1940 was a particularly anxious one. Heavy bombing in High Road, East Finchley and in Ossulton Way on that night resulted in the arrival of ambulances bringing in many casualties. In addition some residents who were shaken and homeless, sought shelter in the hospital.

Some staff worked for several hours without break and others who were off duty returned to assist their colleagues with the influx of casualties. When the building rocketed from nearby explosions and glass splintered around them they worked on unheeding the great danger to themselves.

[19] Finchley Memorial Hospital Your Hospital in War (London Borough of Barnet Archives)

Perhaps the most apt description of conditions that prevailed then can be found in the booklet, Finchley Memorial Hospital Your Hospital in War, where it states: 'It is difficult to convey by description the drama of a casualty hospital at work during an air raid. It has to be experienced. The effect is heightened by the danger common to all, and by the fact that almost all raids are by night'.

Many of the injured suffering from shock were to benefit from the anti-shock treatment and resuscitation technique which staff, on their own initiative, had developed and mastered. Some severely injured from elsewhere were regularly taken by ambulance to the hospital to receive such treatment. Also in place was the excellent blood transfusion service, a credit to many local volunteer blood donors and an X-ray department that functioned all night.

Such height of activity was not continuous. But the internal arrangements for reception and treatment of injured war casualties remained in place, with day and night shifts arranged among the staff in readiness for emergencies.

The general business of the hospital had no less attention, as the different committees continued with their various civilian functions. The Committee of Management ensured all aspects of the hospital remained under close scrutiny. A Hospital Manager was appointed. There were updates on income and expenditure by the Finance Committee and the Building Committee carried out periodic inspection of the hospital building. The Linen League and Ladies Committee continued with the support that ensured the comfort and wellbeing of patients.

Most importantly, the medical team carried on their daily routine of patient care. Finchley residents who were injured elsewhere in the capital returned to the hospital, assured of treatment and attended by their own local doctors. Patients who had operations cancelled during the intense war activity were called in for their treatment.

One instance of this was when the Committee of Management wrote to the Medical Officer of Health in relation to school children scheduled for tonsillectomy operations. Such treatments had to be cancelled prior to the war, but the re-opening of Summerlee Children's ward meant the children could be admitted for their operation.

War alert procedures were maintained right up to the very end, Thursday May 8, 1945, Victory Day in Europe. Credit was expressed to the hospital team in a letter of thanks to the Committee of Management from the Sector Officer based at Mill Hill Barracks which states 'first class help and great collaboration'. [20]

[20] Finchley Memorial Hospital Your Hospital in War

ERAS: Post War

1946 to 1960:
Post War Years:
Voluntary Hospital Systems Abolished
New Funding and Administrative Supervision
New Management Structure
Hospital League of Friends

1962 to 1973:
Era of Development under a National Health Service

1974 to 1982:
Era of Re-organisation
Closure of some services

1983 to 1990:
Barnet Health Authority

1990 to 1999
Era of Reform and modernisation 1990 to 1999:
Barnet Healthcare National Health Service Trust
Friends of the Hospital at Work
Period of Modernisation
Primary Care Groups

Post War Years and National Health Service Act

The immediate post-war era proved a difficult time for the hospital. Some loyal helpers did not return to work after military service, some had moved on after evacuation and others left through ill health or retirement. Added to this was the sheer physical devastation of sections of the building. Much of it required urgent repair and finances were far from adequate to meet the demand.

The Ministry of Health had made some payment to the hospital under the Emergency Hospital Scheme in respect of war casualties but this was not a recurring sum. The King Edward's Hospital Fund for London continued the yearly maintenance grant of £450 and grants were made by Finchley Borough Council and Friern Barnet Urban District Council.

The rising cost in equipment however, and of practically all commodities used in the hospital, meant expenditures were far outweighing income.

It was a period too, when serious consideration was being given to healthcare provision generally. Issues such as how hospital services should be organised, where responsibility for different sections of healthcare should rest, and how to achieve improved healthcare for the population, were all under discussion. The outcome of such deliberations was the National Health Service Act 1946, which received Royal Assent and, on the appointed day, Monday July 5, 1948, the National Health Service came into operation.

Voluntary Hospital System Abolished

Under the Act the voluntary hospital system was abolished and the responsibility for the management and financial upkeep of hospitals under that system, taken over by the State. A tripartite structure of service was established with Hospitals, General Practitioners and Community Services separated from each other. Hospitals were grouped under Regional Hospital Boards, and in that new framework Finchley Memorial Hospital came under the North West Metropolitan Regional Hospital Board.

The fortieth Annual Report of Finchley Memorial Hospital dated December 31, 1947, was the last to be presented under the constitution as a Voluntary Hospital. In that report the Chairman of the Committee of Management, concluded 'It has been our sole aim to serve the interest of patients, and it is our hope that this will remain the fundamental principle under the new regime, and that the Hospital will be enabled to continue, and indeed, extend, its facilities for the benefit of the community which it serves.' [21]

The official Annual Visit of inspection, by visitors appointed by the King Edward's Hospital Fund for London, took place in July of that year. The Visit involved thorough inspection of the hospital, its income and expenditure and its assets and liabilities. The visitors expressed their satisfaction in terms of the smooth running of the affairs of the hospital and of the excellent service to the public. Annual maintenance grant from the King Edward's Hospital Fund for that year, 1947, was recorded as £450.

New Funding and Administrative Supervision

With funding of the hospital now a responsibility of the State, the Hospital Endowment Fund was transferred to the Ministry of Health and placed into a new organisation, namely the National Endowment Fund. An Endowment Commission was set up to distribute sums of money to each hospital in proportion to the number of beds. According to statistical records for the period, January 1, 1948 to July 4, 1948, Finchley Memorial Hospital had 84 beds.

The North West Metropolitan Regional Hospital Board now had the job of supervising the administration and medical policy of the hospital and in the early stages of that new arrangement the hospital was visited by members of that Board. There were compliments from the Board's Chair on the general appearance of the hospital, for the work done from day to day and for the unique character of shared responsibility between Honorary Consulting and Resident Medical staff and local General Practitioners in the management of patient care. Assurances were given that the character of the hospital would not change in the immediate future.

[21] Annual Report of Finchley Memorial Hospital, 31st December, 1947

New Management Structure

Under the Regional structure Finchley Memorial Hospital was now within a group, controlled locally by the Barnet Group Management Committee. Meetings held by the new Management, some attended by representatives of the North West Metropolitan Regional Hospital Board, concerned discussions on aspects such as departmental responsibilities, new staff appointments, work contracts and general administration. Plans for the future development of the hospital also came under discussion and it was against that background that some changes and the expansion of services began.

One new feature was the development of district wide services with hospitals working in groups. A radiotherapy service, for example, provided by Finchley Memorial Hospital, in conjunction with two hospitals in adjoining districts, the Prince of Wales Hospital and Royal Northern Hospital, operated a district wide service, a change which alleviated the long wait for patients for that service.

Hospital League of Friends

The transfer of responsibility for voluntary hospitals did not dampen local interests or the spirit and tradition of support which had existed in communities. Many groups and individuals, formerly supporting their local hospitals, re-organised into Leagues of Friends in a desire to uphold the independent character of their local hospitals. The National League of Hospital Friends was set up in 1949 to facilitate their work.

The League of Friends for Finchley Hospitals was formed in 1957. The Mayor of Finchley in 1957 was Counsellor George Brunskill. He nominated Finchley Memorial Hospital as his designated appeal for that year, inaugurated the League of Friends for Finchley Hospitals and was elected its first chairman. The League was set up to support two hospitals, Finchley Memorial Hospital and St Elizabeth's Hospital in Mayfield Avenue, North Finchley.

The following year, the Golden Anniversary of the hospital was celebrated. The Mayor and Mayoress were in attendance and a special guest amongst the large public gathering was Miss Doris Woodrow who had been present at the opening ceremony in 1908 and was then the young person who had presented a bouquet of flowers to Mrs Homan. [22]

The League of Friends is a registered charity with a wide membership of local residents and an active committee elected from its membership. The aim is to support the work of the hospital by voluntary service and, by raising funds, to provide extra comforts or equipment which will benefit patients who are treated there under the National Health Service.

Fundraising activities, such as the Summer Fete held in the hospital grounds in the month of June each year, and collecting funds at selected locations in the area during the months of April, October and November, have been regular features throughout the years. Legacies from individuals and from former patients add significantly to the Funds thus enabling the League of Friends to achieve their aim. They publish newsletters at regular intervals throughout the year, routinely see to the update of the patients' information leaflet and support joyous occasions for patients such as special birthdays and seasonal occasions like Easter and Christmas. Carol singing is held each Christmas morning in the wards and is a pleasurable event, which culminates with the visit of Father Christmas bearing presents for all inpatients and for the staff.

One early achievement by the League of Friends was raising funds to build a chapel and rest room. The chapel was formerly opened in 1962 and funds were even sufficient to emboss the hymn books with the name of the hospital.

[22] Finchley Press, May 23rd, 1958

1962 to 1973: Era of Development Under a National Health Service

Much headway was made during this period in the quality of health services provided to the local community and in the maintenance and upkeep of facilities at the hospital. A new casualty block and an outpatients department were built and casualty services were extended to provide cover 24 hour of the day. X-ray and physiotherapy departments were improved and day rooms were added to Homan and Woodrow wards.

General Practitioners from Finchley and Friern Barnet became more involved with the day to day activities of the hospital. They ran a casualty service, attended to inpatients, took clinic sessions, served on the management and executive committees and worked with the Resident Medical Officer and the Honorary Consulting staff to address a range of issues and ensure quality patient care.

The hospital was at the forefront of efforts to reduce waiting times for patients, both for outpatients' clinics and admission as in-patients. As early as 1962 a survey was conducted with patients on times of their arrival in outpatient clinics, how long they had waited before they were seen by a consultant, times of their departure from the unit and general satisfaction with the service they received. The transport arrangements for patients who were non-ambulatory were also part of the survey. Waiting lists for inpatient treatments were routinely scrutinised and kept up to date. [23]

Within the National Health Service however, certain issues were emerging about the structure set up to deliver healthcare. In particular were disadvantages of the tripartite system of administration which was apparently causing delays in planning and decision making. There was also growing sense of dissatisfaction with inequity in allocation of resources between services funded by the State and other of similar or complimentary functions funded by Local Authority. By its 20th Anniversary in 1968 discussions were ongoing for the structure to be reviewed.

[23] Minutes of Executive Committee Meeting 1960 to 1964

1974 to 1982:
Era of Re-organisation

Review of the management structure led, in 1974 to a major National Health Service re-organisation. Radically, the Regional Hospital Boards were swept away and in their place Regional, Area and District Health Authorities were created. Within this administrative structure certain services came under one National Health Service umbrella. General Practitioners, hospitals and some of the services previously run by Local Authorities, such as Ambulances, Health Centres, School Health Service, District Nursing, were brought into one system and paid for through central funding. Community Health Councils were established in respect of each District to convey the views of service users to the management and responsible Authority.

The management after re-organisation consisted of Regional, Area and District Health Authorities. But a drawback in this structure was the increase in number of administrators needed to service three tiers of management. By 1979 a Royal Commission on the National Health Service was at work to address the emerging issues and this led in 1982 to the demise of Area Health Authorities.

The responsibility for the planning of all services, in hospitals as well as in the community, became that of District Health Authorities and within all these changes the management of Finchley Memorial Hospital became that of Barnet Health Authority. The hospital at that period consisted of 124 beds, a casualty service run by local General Practitioners was in operation and the healthcare provided to the community was defined as partly acute.

Closure of some Services

During the period a decision was taken to close the children's ward. A principal driver for the decision was the low occupancy, and the difficulty of engaging services of a paediatrician on a regular basis.

The Ear, Nose and Throat unit was closed. With just 13 beds, it was insufficient to justify the proper staffing level recommended by the Department of Health. Facilities were poor and the unit was not properly equipped to accommodate the extra number of beds that would be required. Patients for that service were in future referred to the Royal Free Hospital in Hampstead.

The number of surgical operations performed at the hospital was in decline and discussion was ongoing as to the future of the operating theatre. A new surgical department, under construction at Barnet General Hospital, was nearing completion and on the opening of that block all surgical work was transferred and the operating theatre at Finchley closed.

The hospital pharmacy closed and the service re-located as a result of centralisation of pharmaceutical services generally.

Closure of the Casualty Service was proposed. The service, run by local General Practitioners, was provided twenty four hours per day and the closure proposal raised public concern. The Community Health Council, the organisation set up in 1974 to represent the interests of the local community, raised the issue of public concern with the Health Authority and the substantial variation in the current service that would be the likely outcome.

Recognising that the main argument advanced for the proposed closure was that of finance, that alternative facilities were not at the time satisfactory and the adverse effects of closure, especially for local schools, the Community Health Council expressed the view that the Casualty Department should, in the interest of patients, remain open. [24]

---

[24] Minutes of Community Health Council Meeting, February 7th, 1977

In that year the Hospital Summer Fete, organised by the League of Friends, May 28, 1977, was a very special one. Celebrating twenty years of involvement with the hospital, the League was in the process of raising funds to take on one of its biggest project, the provision of two day rooms for patients of Dickens and Fallowfield wards.

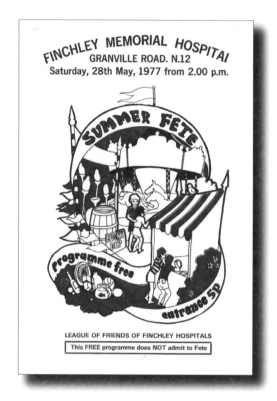

In 1979 St Elizabeth's Hospital in Mayfield Avenue closed and the League of Friends for Finchley Hospitals became the Friends of Finchley Memorial Hospital.

The hospital chapel was hardly in use. Only few patients were well enough to attend services so chaplains were regularly taking services on the wards instead of in the chapel. It was finally closed in 1980 and from 1982 the space was used as a Mother and Baby Clinic for a short period and then later set up as the wheelchair clinic.

Barnet Health Authority
1983 to 1990

Under Barnet Health Authority management, and during a period when more emphasis on the strengthening of primary care services was advocated, some quite significant changes in provision of healthcare at Finchley Memorial Hospital were proposed.

The most far reaching, contained in *Barnet Health Authority Consultative Document on Future Development and Re-distribution of Services 1984 to 1986*, was the proposal to transfer all acute medical and surgical work to Barnet General Hospital and to establish Finchley Memorial Hospital as a centre of medical services for the elderly.

In order to facilitate that objective a Geriatric Day Hospital with capacity to care for thirty patients was proposed at Finchley. It was envisaged that the service would work in conjunction with the Medical Assessment and Treatment Unit based at Barnet General Hospital. [25]

The proposals were adopted and changes and re-development of services went ahead rapidly. Beds made vacant by the transfer of acute treatment to Barnet General Hospital were re-designated to care of the elderly, and improvements were made to rehabilitative and supporting services that would better meet the needs of elderly patients.

Inpatient care with a 90 bed capacity was also put in place on four wards, George Brunskill, Marjory Warren, Fallowfield and Dickens wards.

The Geriatric Day Hospital was ready for occupation in late 1986 with official opening in January 1987 by Mrs Margaret Thatcher then Prime Minister and Member of Parliament for Finchley. The layout included in its setting a glazed conservatory which overlooked a pretty triangular garden, all donated by the Hospital Friends.

[25] Barnet Health Authority Consultative Document of Future Development and Redistribution of Services 1984 to 1986

The following year the annual fete organised by the Friends, took the form of an anniversary celebration of the hospital's 80th year of service to the community. Included in the celebration was a party for patients, their relatives, volunteers and guests. Members of staff and of the Friends all joined in the activities, and pupils from nearby Finchley Manorhill School sang Beatle's songs. A special birthday cake was cut by one of the patients. [26]

[26] Hendon and Finchley Times, June 23, 1988

1990 to 1999 Era of Reforms and Modernisation

A new era dawned for Finchley Memorial Hospital when a programme of reforms in the way hospitals would be managed was introduced in the National Health Service. The reforms, enshrined in the Community Care Act 1990, heralded the introduction of the internal market with separation of the responsibility for the funding and for the provision of services, the award of self-governing status to some hospitals and changes in organisational management of health service nationwide. The changes, aimed to improve quality and efficiency of services provided to patients, were stated as 'more fundamental than any experienced since its inception in 1948'. [27]

The changes were implemented nationwide on April 1, 1991 with main functions of the District Health Authorities becoming that of assessing needs of their resident population and the purchasing of services to meet those needs. Locally the implementation gave birth to two directly managed units, the General Hospital and Community Health Service units, both under the management of Barnet Health Authority.

Barnet Healthcare National Health Service Trust

In that structure Finchley Memorial Hospital came under the jurisdiction of the newly established Barnet Healthcare National Health Service Trust. [28]

The Trust was established on November 1st, 1991 and came into operation April 1st 1992. To meet the requirements of the reforms the Trust set out some quite far reaching changes to the management and functioning of Finchley Memorial Hospital. Almost immediately, the administration was reorganised and staffing levels reviewed, with drastic reduction in the workforce.

To further develop the plans for the hospital as a centre for medicine for the elderly, changes were made to the use of some wards. Dickens and Fallowfield wards were designated for patients needing Continuing Care for long term illness and George Brunskill and Marjory Warren wards for Respite care and Rehabilitation. The number of beds for inpatients then stood at 90. However the number of beds required for provision of Continuing Care was revised and Fallowfield ward with 14 beds was closed.

---

[27] The New National Health Service: Organisation and Management, National Association of Health Authorities and Trusts, 1990
[28] Statutory Instructions 1991 No 2322, National Health Service, England and Wales

A range of outpatient services continued under Barnet Healthcare Trust management. These included X-ray and physiotherapy services, outpatient clinics that offered consultations in different specialities and a minor casualty department managed by local General Practitioners. Primary care services included speech therapy, family planning, child health clinic, colostomy advice and incontinence care. [29]

The hospital was also the base for an Out of Hours General Practitioner service provided to local residents. Known as Barndoc, it was launched in 1996 by a cooperative of local General Practitioners who agreed to share the care and treatment of patients outside normal surgery hours. It was accessible by telephone or face to face consultations during the hours of 7pm to 10pm on weekdays and 8pm to 10pm on weekends and Bank Holidays.

[29] Barnet Healthcare NHS Trust: A Basic Guide to Health Care for patients attending Finchley Memorial Hospital 1994/1995 Edition

Friends of the Hospital at Work

The Hospital Friends continued their support and active involvement during the 1990s. In the midst of all the changes, they were the mainstay in holding together the important connection between the local community and the hospital. Funds were raised for new equipment, for general maintenance and upkeep and to assist with the cost on new building and refurbishment.

A casualty block, opened in October 1992 by Mrs Margaret Thatcher, Member of Parliament for Finchley, was funded in large part by the Friends. They also funded the design and layout of a pretty garden overlooking the rehabilitation wards. School children from nearby Finchley Manorhill School assisted in placing a time capsule in a central plinth within the reception area, also financed by the Friends.

As part of the National Health Service 50th Anniversary celebrations nationwide, Barnet Healthcare Trust together with the Friends, held an Open Week at the hospital, Monday 1st to Friday 5th June 1998. Local residents were invited to view their hospital, meet and talk with staff and to discover the wealth of facilities provided. Highlighted throughout the week was the work of the Friends, their contribution towards enhancing the hospital environment and the amenities provided by them to help further the delivery of best quality care for patients.

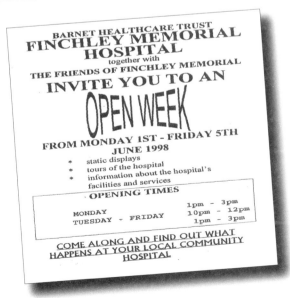

BARNET HEALTHCARE TRUST
FINCHLEY MEMORIAL HOSPITAL
together with
THE FRIENDS OF FINCHLEY MEMORIAL
INVITE YOU TO AN

OPEN WEEK

FROM MONDAY 1ST - FRIDAY 5TH
JUNE 1998
* static displays
* tours of the hospital
* information about the hospital's facilities and services

OPENING TIMES

MONDAY		1pm - 3pm
TUESDAY - FRIDAY		10pm - 12pm
		1pm - 3pm

COME ALONG AND FIND OUT WHAT
HAPPENS AT YOUR LOCAL COMMUNITY
HOSPITAL

Period of Modernisation

In line with changes in the Health Service nationwide, the hospital was soon to undergo further changes in its management. The Government White Paper: *The New NHS Modern Dependable,* issued December 1997, signalled the abolishment of the internal market that was enshrined in the Community Care Act 1990. That system, it was claimed, created competition and was an obstacle to modernising the health service. In its place were plans for an integrated system designed to move from competition to cooperation, to equity in provision and to the establishment of good working relationship between all health agencies, social services and local communities. [30]

Primary Care Groups

In addition to national standards and guidelines for service and treatment set out in that White Paper, a new framework was introduced for the establishment of Primary Care Groups. This framework required General Practitioners, Community Nurses and other primary and community care professionals to work together to plan and shape services for patients and to promote the health of the local population. [31]

Three Primary Care Groups, North, West and South, were set up on April 1, 1999 by Barnet Healthcare Trust. Finchley Memorial Hospital was located in the North locality which included the areas of East Barnet, Hadley, Arkley, Totteridge, Whetstone, Friern Barnet and Brunswick Park.

Barnet Health Authority, in this new arrangement, held overall responsibility for the commissioning of services to improve the health and wellbeing of the residents. In its *Commissioning Proposal Document, 1998/1999,* Finchley Memorial Hospital was mentioned as a well located site for a substantial population and one that was already providing a large number of complimentary functions such as X-ray, General Practitioners out of hours cooperative and a minor accident and treatment centre. It was also noted in that document that the hospital enjoyed considerable public support and was probably the most appropriately positioned site of all those owned by the Community Healthcare Trust. [32]

---

[30] Department of Health: The New NHS Modern Dependable December 1997
[31] NHS Executive Health Service Circular Series Number HSC1998/021, February 25th, 1998
[32] Barnet Health Authority Commissioning Proposals 1998/1999

Into the
Twenty First Century:

Into the Twenty First Century

Managerial responsibility for the hospital was about to change yet again as proposals were put forward for a move to the status of Primary Care Trust. Such a move would combine the functions of the three Primary Care Groups. It would also bring General Practitioners, District Nurses, Health Visitors and other healthcare clinicians working in the community into a single group, and would be a free standing National Health Service organisation, locally managed and having more control over its own affairs.

To this end Barnet Community Healthcare Trust, in collaboration with Barnet Health Authority and the three Primary Care Groups began talks, informally at first, as to the benefits locally in pursuing the move to Primary Care Trust. [33]

The follow-up was a second document setting out the reasons for change, explanation of how a new organisation would work and the benefits to patients and staff. This document, the formal consultation, was circulated and public meetings held in different community settings during the months of July to November 2000 to seek the views of the local community. [34]

The Hospital managed by Barnet Primary Care Trust

Barnet Primary Care Trust came into operation on August 1, 2001 and assumed managerial responsibility for the three Primary Care Groups and two hospitals, Edgware Community Hospital and Finchley Memorial Hospital.

Healthcare provision at Finchley Memorial Hospital at this period included a vast range of services for both inpatients and outpatients. Inpatient services included intermediate care and rehabilitation with aim to promote recovery and to prevent admission to acute hospital. Wards in operation were Marjory Warren, a 28 bed ward with particular focus on orthopaedic rehabilitation, George Brunskill ward also with 28 beds for Stroke rehabilitation and Dickens ward with 20 beds for patients needing continuing care for long term conditions.

[33] Development of Primary Care Trust in Barnet, An Informal Discussion Document March 2000
[34] What's Best for Barnet? A proposal to establish Primary Care Trust in Barnet

The Day Hospital provided, upon referral, assessment by a multi-disciplinary team and patients offered treatment either in the day hospital or in their own homes. Attendance at the Day Hospital was up to 20 patients each day, Tuesdays, Wednesdays and Thursdays with an outreach service offered Mondays and Fridays.

Patients attending the Day Hospital as well as inpatients had access to social work support and to therapy services such as occupational and physiotherapy, speech and language therapy, dietetics and nutrition advice.

The Minor Injuries Unit run by group of local General Practitioners and supported by Nursing Staff remained operational, providing access to prompt unscheduled care 9am to 7pm everyday. Attendance to the Unit approximated 25,000 per year.

Other services provided included diagnostic and clinical support services, X-ray and radiotherapy, phlebotomy (blood testing) and ultra-sound, orthopaedic, diabetic and gynaecology clinics, learning disability, paediatric therapies and child adolescent and mental health services.

Barndoc, the General Practitioner cooperative, remained on site providing out of hours services evenings and weekends. A welcoming addition for children was a toy library and play space made available through aid from the London Borough of Barnet.

The hospital also remained the base for a number of services provided for all of Barnet. These included Continence promotion, Stoma care, wheelchair service and equipment store. [35]

[35] Monitoring Reports on level of activity at Finchley Memorial Hospital, prepared by Hospital Adminsistrator

Recognising Excellence

The treatment for stroke rehabilitation at Finchley Memorial Hospital earned national recognition when in 2000 and again in 2001 the hospital received the Department of Health Beacon Award for quality of work. The relevant criteria for such an award included efficient organisation of work, regard for meeting both medical and social needs of patients, attention to all aspects of the patient's day in hospital, ensuring their comfort and wellbeing and giving that personal care and attention which individual patients may from time to time require.

There was also favourable comment in the *Clinical Governance Review, July 2003* by the Commission for Health Improvement regarding the work of the staff in relation to dignity and respect as experienced by patients in their care.

Barndoc, the 'out of hours' General Practitioner Service with its nursing team also gained recognition as one of the best in the country and was awarded the National Health Service Acorn Award for clinical governance.

A New White Paper

Change was on the way again for Finchley Memorial Hospital when in January 2006 the Government White Paper titled *'Our Health, Our Care, Our Say, a New Direction for Community Services'*, was published. The White Paper envisaged the provision of good quality healthcare and social care services in locations near to people's homes and for the avoidance of hospital admissions unless absolutely necessary. [36]

The hospital, it appears, was already recognised as being in a unique position to be part of that vision. Barnet Primary Care Trust, in its *Strategic Service Development Plan 2005-2008*, mentioned the hospital as the main hub to serve North and South Localities and as such would be central to a service delivery model that would bring care closer to patients. However, in that document it was also stated that the hospital was far from ideal in terms of its fabric, design and functionality and that options for long term development were being prepared. [37]

[36] Government White Paper: Our Health Our Care Our Say, a new Direction for Community Services, 2006
[37] Barnet Primary Care Trust Strategic Development Plan 2005 to 2008

New Service Development

The hospital was now in the forefront of plans by Barnet Primary Care Trust to develop a new model of service for rehabilitation and intermediate care. Defined as a 'Single Point of Access', (see diagram below) the model provided for a more patient-centred response to referrals with rapid access to multidisciplinary assessment and screening and to prompt diagnostic and specialist opinion. The involvement of supporting services such as the voluntary sector and social services were part of the model.

The changes were much in line with the Department of Health Guidance on models that would actively promote health, coordinate care across professional disciplines, support patients in the community and for the avoidance of admission to acute hospital beds. Where admission became necessary, the plan was for well supported discharge arrangements to be put in place, thus enabling patients to return home with confidence and retain their independence.

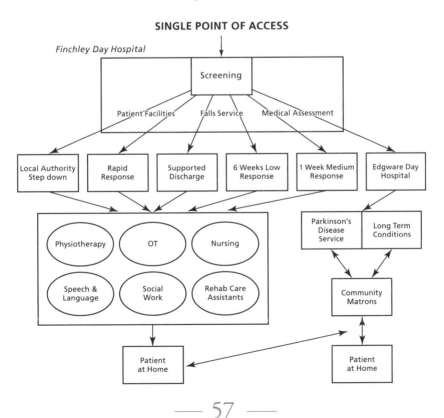

SINGLE POINT OF ACCESS

One significant change during the present period was the closure of Dickens Ward which catered to patients needing continuous care. Dickens Ward was well managed. In 2004, the nursing team received a clinical team achievement award in recognition of their hard work and dedication to patient care. The decision to close the ward was however inevitable given the difficulties encountered in adequately meeting the care standards set out for such service in the government modernisation plan. An example was the requirement of single rooms with en suite facilities. The proposed closure was preceded by public consultation as to the best option for patients and their carers. In the end, patients were moved to local nursing homes and closure went ahead reducing the number of inpatient beds to 56. The ward was eventually refurbished to accommodate the single point of access team.

The Hospital and its Community

Throughout all the changes the Friends of the hospital remained consistent in their aim to ensure the comfort and wellbeing of patients. Improvements across a range of social and clinical activities have been supported by them. Expenditure on medical equipment, upgrades of nurses stations, purchase of treatment chairs and specialised wheelchairs, the renewal of televisions in the wards and day room have all happened through the Friends.

One major undertaking was the complete refurbishment of the Minor Injuries Unit to provide a more welcoming environment for patients, improve the seating and providing the staff with modern equipment in the work station. The Time Capsule which had been placed by pupils at nearby Finchley Manorhill school (now Compton school) in 1992 had to be removed during the refurbishment but was stored securely and then replaced.

NHS Walk-in Centre

The minor injuries unit is now formally the NHS Walk-in Centre offering fast and convenient access to a range of services, health information and treatment of minor illnesses. The service is predominantly nurse-led with nurse practitioners and staff working in a team to ensure majority of attendances are seen within the officially set target time. Opening hours have been extended by four hours per day providing improved patient access to healthcare. [38]

A new Phlebotomy (blood testing) Clinic, opened in 2004, also owes its improvement to the commitment and tireless efforts of the Friends. The 50th anniversary of the Friends was marked by a special hospital Fete in 2007.

[38] Talkback, Issue 33, Autumn 2007: Newsletter for staff of the Primary Care Trust

Involving the Community

One responsibility of Primary Care Trusts is to ensure involvement of local communities in the shaping of local health services and that their views are sought when planning for changes in provision, re-design or development. One initiative by Barnet Primary Care Trust to meet that responsibility has been publication of a bi-monthly newsletter *'Local People in Health'* with information on its activities and invitations to interested residents to become involved in aspects of the service.

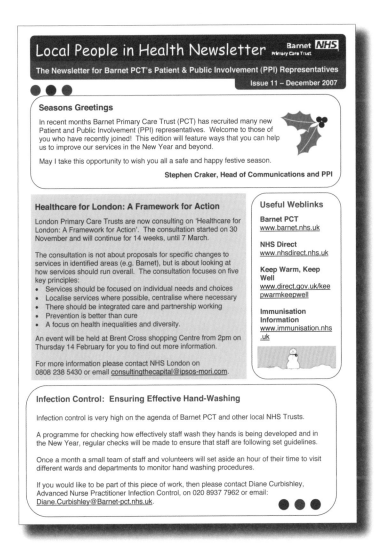

Finchley Memorial Hospital has benefited from this through information placed in the public arena through the newsletter. The refurbishment of the Outpatients Department and Walk-in-Centre for examples, were projects of which local residents were informed and invited to contribute to the planning. [39]

Other publications through which the community are kept informed include Finchley Memorial Hospital Magazine, made available through the support of various local charities, the Barnet Primary Care Trust Annual Report and Guide to Local Health Services. There are also the much publicised Board meetings of the Trust to which the public are invited.

Barnet NHS
Primary Care Trust

Members of the public and staff are invited to attend the Trust Board meeting of

Barnet Primary Care Trust
To be held in public on

Thursday 28 June 2007
1.00pm - 4.00pm

Education Centre,
Edgware Community Hospital,
Burnt Oak Broadway, Edgware, HA8 0AD

1:00-1:15 there will be an open session, for members of the public to raise items

1:15 start of Board Meeting

For copies of the agenda or further information please contact Corporate Services on 020 8937 7952 / 7975

www.barnet.nhs.uk

SMOKEFREE Want FREE help and advice to quit smoking?
Ring the Stop Smoking Service on **0800 32 82 784**

---

[39] Local People in Health Newsletter, May 2005

The Present and into the Future

Finchley Memorial is presently a very busy hospital. Data on levels of activity up to 2005 show 96% occupancy of inpatient beds. There were 1,400 visits to the Day Hospital and 14,000 visits to X-ray and other diagnostic services. 9,276 visits were made to Outpatients clinic, 30,000 visits to the Walk-in-Centre and 35,000 to the Phlebotomy Clinic. There were 2,400 visits to the Diabetic Clinic and 1,300 to speech and language sessions. Barndoc, the Out-of-Hours General Practitioners service had 33,000 phone calls and 11,000 attendances face to face. [40]

There has been much publicity in the local press as to the future of the hospital. The Press, Hendon and Finchley Edition, reported on March 17, 2005 of plans being drawn up for major re-development of Finchley Memorial Hospital.
On November 16, 2006 the Hendon and Finchley Times reported on proposals to re-develop the Community Hospital. The Potters Bar Press, June 21, 2007 reported that re-development of the hospital had been given the go ahead by Barnet Council.

Most significantly however, set out in the *Strategic Outline Case of Barnet Primary Care Trust March 2007* are proposals for a major redevelopment of Finchley Memorial Hospital through a new build programme. Taking forward this proposal is an inclusive project team of local National Health Service organisations, Local Council, community organisations and one fundamental component, involvement of the local community.

---

[40] A Strategic Outline Case to develop a Network of Community and Primary Care Services; North and South of Barnet: Barnet Primary Care Trust, March 2007

End of an Era

End of an Era

In 2008 the hospital, first as a Cottage Hospital and then as Finchley Memorial Hospital, will have served 100 years in the provision of healthcare to the local community. It has braved the challenges of two world wars. It has come through financial difficulties and surmounted the numerous changes in management, the new policies for healthcare and astonishing advances in medicine and medical technology. The changing attitudes on issues of health and healthcare and the new demands that such changes bring have been faced with courage, and it has grown close to the heart of its local Community.

Thanks to its geographical location and its current service model, it has been recognised as well placed to be of significant importance in the new direction of community healthcare and shaping of health services locally.

Barnet Primary Care Trust in its *Commissioning Prospectus,* 2008 /2009 states that one of the most significant initiatives for Barnet residents is the proposal to develop Finchley Memorial Hospital and that the hospital, which primarily serves the North and South of the Borough of Barnet, will soon be redeveloped. In the future, it will continue to offer the range of services currently provided, but with new services being added to help provide more patient choice and better care for the local community. [41]

[41] Patient Commissioning Prospectus 2008/2009: Barnet Primary Care Trust

Conclusion

Conclusion

This brief history cannot forecast the future. It can however act as a timely reminder of the role of our predecessors. Local people worked together to build a hospital and gave it their support through years of war, of hardship, and of change. Awareness of such a legacy should give a humbling sense of responsibility to ensure it continues in the future to the benefit of the community it serves.

It was in May 1908 at the opening ceremony, that the first president and generous benefactor Mr Ebenezer Homan, in his address to the audience said the following 'the work has been undertaken and brought to completion, the utility of which is beyond the range of controversy and the way in which it has been accomplished is the strongest possible proof that the neighbours around realised the fact and acted accordingly. They made up their minds that the thing should be done and went to work with a will'. [42]

Dorrell Dressekie
May 2008

---

[42] The Finchley Press, May 23, 1958 'citizen' reviews a bit of history on when the cottage hospital was opened 50 years ago

Finchley Memorial Hospital

Memories, Views and Anecdotal
Comments

Memories, Views and Anecdotal Comments

The comments, views and reminiscences on record here are a random selection from a range of sources, some given verbally, some in written form and some through short interviews. The sources include local residents, patients and some relatives and carers, some former and some current employees, members of the Friends, members of Friern Barnet Local History Society, local Councillors and hospital managers. An informative source has also been readers' letters from the Opinion Page of some local newspapers.

The Emergency Service at Finchley Memorial Hospital has been my saviour a number of times. The children are now all grown up so it's a long time ago. But I remember well, my son, he must have just turned two years of age then, was in the garden with cup of juice, and in the process of drinking he was stung in the mouth by a wasp. He was screaming, his mouth swelling. Luckily for us a nurse living next door came to our rescue, and advised a dash to the emergency department at Finchley Memorial Hospital. After that incident we went there other times with minor injuries, more times than I can recall now. What I remember well though, is that we were never turned away, and always treated with kindness and a smile.

I visited that hospital with my two children as babies, there was a baby clinic, nice and friendly place it was and I had good advice. Is a clinic still there? My children are now 23 and 24 years old so it would have been in the 1980s.

I attended Finchley Memorial Hospital over a period of some weeks for physiotherapy treatment. I was referred there from Barnet General Hospital orthopaedic department where I attended following a skiing accident in which I injured my knee. The injury was described to me as a tear in an Anterior Cruciate Ligament and I was put on the waiting list to have my knee repaired. This was in 1988; I was in my early twenties, a lover of sports and had no idea how long I would have to be on a waiting list. I was quite distressed and began to think my days of playing any type of sport was over until I could have the operation. The option offered me in the interim was to have some physiotherapy.

This proved a most amazing experience for me. The physiotherapist I met at Finchley Memorial Hospital did not focus on an operation at some future date. She explained my injury and assured me that by working on strengthening and regaining flexibility in my knee I could rehabilitate it and continue to play many sports. She showed great concern for me and was always positive as we worked together with that aim. I was working in Central London at the time and was concerned about getting to work, but she arranged for me a flexible treatment schedule so I could attend the sessions quite early in the morning and still arrive at my job in reasonable time.

My daughter was a patient in that hospital many years ago. If everyone spoke of it as highly as she did then it must be the happiest place in England.

I was at that hospital with my small son, only a few months ago. He was vomiting and I was worried it could go on all night. I was surprised to find it was my own doctor in the Out-of-Hours clinic. I remember we did not wait long and there was no rush. I made a note to myself that this is the place to come anytime in the future for good care and understanding.

I still have the scar on my chin. When I was seven, which would have been 1951, I was playing in the garden of a school friend who lived in Friary Road N12. I remember it was a Saturday morning and we were playing what we called "off-ground he" in those days - what is it called now, tag? In an effort to evade my pursuer I jumped on the rockery where I slipped and gashed the underneath of my chin. My friend's father, who was a chemist in Finchley, came to my aid with bandages. I then recall been taken home in nearby Torrington Park where my parents were aghast at the large cut which was bleeding profusely. My friend's father had a black Ford Consul, and he conveyed me with my parents to Finchley Memorial Hospital Casualty Department where I was examined and operated on in the theatre. I know I was given general anaesthetic so I remember nothing of the operation but I was told I had nine stitches. I remember coming home in the afternoon and emptying the contents of my stomach on the kerb outside my home. My parents praised me for holding it until I got out of the car. Here on my chin, I have the scars to this day. I may be wrong about this but think the Casualty Department was on the right of the building as one faces the front entrance.

Pleased to add a little to the collecting tin, doing a great job collecting to support that hospital. It is years ago now, but I used to help with the mobile library going round the wards with books on a trolley, mostly large print books. My doctor sent me there recently for a blood test, there has been a lot of changes.

These people here, all of them, seems they can't do enough for us, I thank them all, that's all I can say.

I joined the Ladies' Circle in 1969. Activities of the Ladies' Circle then, included the running of stalls at the Summer Fete. Soon after joining the chairman looked me in the eye and told me the Circle would be running a cake stall at the Fete and she required me to bake 12 cakes. Twelve cakes I thought, that can't be too bad, twelve fairy cakes would be easy. Horror was to follow when I realised she meant twelve full size cakes. I have never again achieved that amount of baking! The Ladies' circle was famous for its cakes. Such was the fame that they always sold out quickly, dust the cake crumbs from the stand and finish in time to enjoy the rest of the day at the Fete. Another famous stall for the Circle was that of hats. I have happy memories of running that stall, a table full with a selection of beautiful hats sold out to eager buyers in no time at all.

As a mother of three boisterous boys it seemed I was always at Finchley Memorial Hospital with an injured boy needing a stitch or a tetanus jab. Many times I have thought I should have a season ticket to the Walk-in Department. In those days it was a very quiet department, nurses met you on entry and you were treated with care and kindness.

I do think it was a well kept secret by those who were fortunate to be in the know. Finchley Memorial Hospital was the place to get the best speedy treatment, kindness, no queues and the best staff who were happy to look after their patients.

My young son was rushed to that hospital from his school, Friern Barnet County School in Hemmington Avenue. This was about 1970 or 1971. He had fallen from a climbing frame and damaged his leg. The school called me at work and I rushed to the hospital. The X-ray confirmed a fracture. As far as I can recall there was no delay in him having treatment, his leg was put in plaster, he came home after two days in the hospital and I had to take him there for checks till his leg mended and the plaster removed. I think my son was liking the visits, it was better than going to school.

I knew of the hospital, but it was not until I came along to an Open Day that I realised how much work goes on there. I feel it is a real asset to the Community and I now support the Friends.

But for the work and dedication of the Friends I don't think the hospital would survive. The amount of equipment they purchase, foot the bill for refurbishment, plant a lovely garden, quite amazing! I doubt whether the management fully recognise the extent of their input.

I went to the Walk-in-Centre for some advice. A friend told me about the centre, I did not know it existed. I saw a nurse, it was all very confidential and her advice proved helpful for me. It was just a short visit.

Finchley Memorial Hospital was where we took children for emergency treatment when I worked at Oak Lodge Special School. We were always seen promptly and the staff showed great understanding of the needs of the children we cared for. Being also quite near to the school meant very little travel with sometimes quite an anxious child and concerned parent.

My father passed away there. He had very good care, but now it is too emotional for me to talk, might start to cry, sorry.

I have been coming here once a week, taken here by ambulance. Everyone is very nice and I am near the end of my treatment. I hope to manage at home with all the help and advice I have been getting, will miss it but I make room for someone else.

Retired now and did think about joining the Friends, have not done so yet but intend to. I am aware they contribute quite substantially to this hospital, and both patients and staff benefit from their work.

Finchley Memorial Hospital had the most beautiful gardens at one time. I lived nearby in a house overlooking part of the gardens and it was always a pleasure to look out at the colours in bloom. I have used the emergency service too, had to take my daughter there after an incident at school.

My doctor sent me there for a blood test. I was seen promptly, the only wait was for the result of the test to get back to my doctor. Why that was I don't know.

I want to highlight the work been done at the hospital. My elderly mother recently lost her battle for life while a patient there, but through exceptionally caring and supportive staff, her final days were made easier for her and for relatives. The hospital also has some unsung heroes, those who do the cleaning. In an old hospital which is literally crumbling away, the ward was kept remarkably clean, in comparison to newer hospitals I have visited. The cleaners were charming, respectful and they always had a smile and a kind word. It is very good news that Finchley Memorial Hospital is to be re-developed.

Hospital Matrons

1908   Miss A Clark

1912   Miss M Torry

1916   Miss C Maple

1920   Miss N Hall

1922   Miss K Firth

1922   Miss N George

1925   Miss M Camp

1941   Miss C Jenkins

1945   Miss D Owen

1960   Miss A McDougall

The post of matron was abolished when the structure on nursing hierarchy changed

Matrons, now classified as Modern Matrons were resumed in 2005

2005: Debbie Donnelly

2005 to present: Nicola Perkins, Nursing Matron

2007 to present: Elise Warner, Therapy Matron

Finchley Memorial Hospital Plaques

Finchley Memorial Hospital Plaques

WOODSIDE CLUB BED.

CHILD WELFARE COT.

THIS COT WAS ENDOWED BY THE FRIERN BARNET CIVIL DEFENCE SERVICES EMERGENCY BENEFIT FUND 1939 – 1945

EAST FINCHLEY WESLEYAN CHURCH COT.

THE PRUDENTIAL ASSURANCE Co Ltd SUBSCRIBE ANNUALLY TOWARDS THE SUPPORT OF THIS BED

ENDOWED BY THE CITIZENS OF THE BOROUGH IN APPRECIATION OF THE WORK OF ALL BRANCHES OF THE FINCHLEY CIVIL DEFENCE SERVICES 1939 – 1945.

MARGARET DAVIE COT.

NORTH FINCHLEY CONGREGATIONAL CHURCH BED

WAPLE BED.

SUMMERLEE WARD
TO COMMEMORATE THE SUMMERLEE
V.A.D. WAR HOSPITAL 1915–1919
DR. T. W. HICKS, M.B.E., J.P.
OFFICER IN COMMAND.
MR. C. W. ANDREW,
QUARTERMASTER AND HON. SECRETARY.

THE FINCHLEY TRADERS' BED
PRESENTED BY
THE CHURCH END FINCHLEY CHAMBER OF COMMERCE
1928

– THE –
J. C. TURPIN
— COT —

THE
FRANK HONEGGER
BED
1936

THIS BED
IS BEING MAINTAINED
BY THE CHILDREN OF THE
FINCHLEY ELEMENTARY SCHOOLS

NAVARINO COT

ODEON
MICKEY MOUSE
CLUB COT
1937

THIS BED
IS ENDOWED
TO THE MEMORY OF
GEORGE SCARFE,
BY HIS SISTERS
ISIDORA & ELLEN.

EAST FINCHLEY
CONGREGATIONAL CHURCH
BED.

THIS BED
IS BEING MAINTAINED
BY THE
FINCHLEY CARNIVAL FUND.